OXFORD ANTHEMS
General Editor David Willcocks

THREE ANTHEMS
No. 2

Come, Holy Ghost, the Maker

A98

From Hymns and Songs
of the Church
No. 44, Verse 1

by George Wither
(1588 - 1667)

CEDRIC THORPE DAVIE
(1937)

Poco più mosso

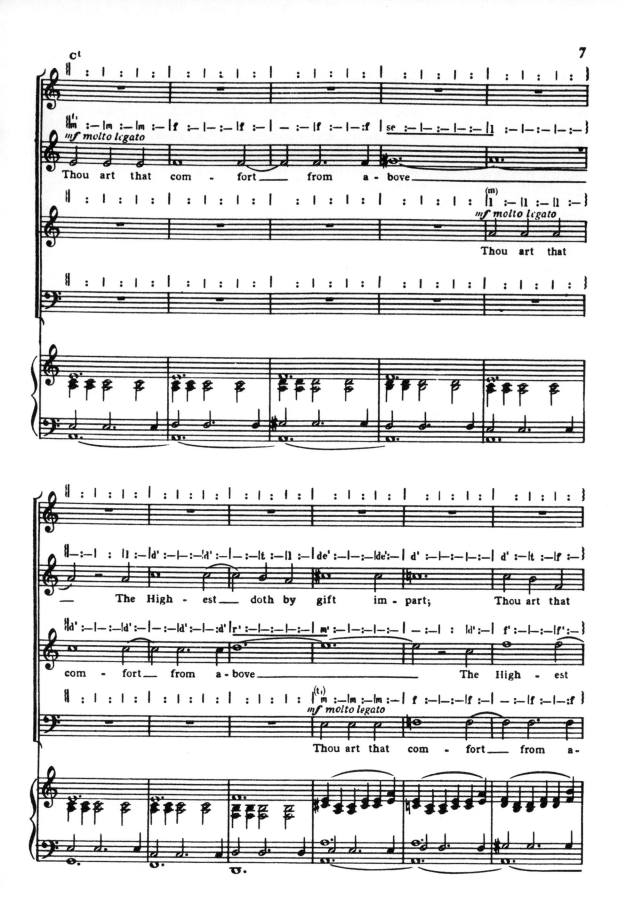

mf molto legato

Thou art that com - fort _____ from a-

com - fort The High - est _____ doth by gift im -

_____ doth by gift im - part, _____ by gift im -

- bove _____ The High - est

simile

- bove _____ Thou art that

- part; Thou art that com - fort, that

- part; Thou art that com - fort, that

doth by gift im - part; Thou _____

(add)

Tempo I

Reproduced and printed by
Halstan & Co. Ltd., Amersham, Bucks., England

OXFORD UNIVERSITY PRESS

ISBN 0 19 350158 9